FOREWORD

As the second Annihilation book concludes the epic Dark Age saga of Scotland's ultimate protector, the country's cultural future lies in the balance between nostalgic remembrance and the dynamism of a new identity.

When a people are subdued they turn to the legends of history for nourishment as it is the great deeds of heroes past that bring solace in the darkest times. But it is just as relevant to look to the future and the aspirations of a society's youth for inspiration.

Scotland is a vibrant place. A country of three languages, immense history, celebrated tradition and burgeoning creativity. A nation ready to reinvent itself on the world stage, projecting a new found confidence to an intrigued and watchful audience.

Saltire and Diamondsteel Comics are at the forefront of this change as Scotland's cultural references move from "tartan cringe" to "Caledonian cool".

Welcome to the next generation.

John Ferguson
18th March 2015

"A people without faith in themselves cannot survive."
Ancient Proverb

SALTIRE

N

CAVE GIANTS

LORDS OF THE ISLES

HUNTERS OF THE FIELDS

MOUNTAIN RUNNERS

MOUNTAIN OF ETHER

HIGHLANDS OF SHADOW

LOST GLEN

DEEP FOREST SHAMANS

INO - ENTRY TO THE ETHEREAL WORLD

LAND OF THE SEERS

ADD - ENTRY TO THE OTHERWORLD

FRONTIER WALL

MEN OF THE LOCH

RIVER DWELLERS

VALLEYS OF LIGHT

HILL TRIBE

WOODLAND FOLK

...THE SCOTTISH BORDER...
SALTIRE
ANNIHILATION
PART 2
...THE MERCYAN ARMY.
TEAR THE LIFE FROM THIS LAND...
...SEAR THE MARK OF MERCYAN INTO THEIR BONES.
THE ENDS OF THE EARTH OPENS ITS DOORS TO DESTRUCTION. A KING SHALL RISE UNCHALLENGED BY THE DAWN.
RECLAIM MY HELMET FROM THAT WRETCH IN THE NORTH...
...DO NOT FAIL ME BOY!
CHAAARGE!!!
WRITER: JOHN FERGUSON ARTIST: CLAIRE ROE COLOURIST: LAUREN KNIGHT LETTERER: PHILLIP VAUGHAN
THE SAVAGES HAVE FLED! HA!
TOO FEEBLE TO STAND AND FIGHT...
...BEHOLD, THE MIGHT OF THE MERCYAN!
COVER: JAMES DEVLIN EDITOR: CLARE FERGUSON ART EDITOR: PHILLIP VAUGHAN
PUBLISHER: DIAMONDSTEEL COMICS EDITOR IN CHIEF: JOHN FERGUSON

THE HILL TRIBE!
A NEW THREAT BECKONS.
I SENSE IT TOO.
GUARDIANS OF LIGHT, THE ETHEREAL STAFF CALLS TO YOU ONCE MORE.
BE SWIFT... AS DISTRACTION BLINDS, WE ARE CAUGHT UNAWARE.
CENNET LEADS THE WAY AS HE WORRIES FOR THE VULNERABLE HILL TRIBE ON THE BORDER.
HOLD!
...THE EAGLE SPEAR PLEADS CAUTION.
THE MERCYAN STRIKES WITH OUR DEFENCES STRETCHED AND OUR PEOPLE SCATTERED.
WE ARE OVERLY HOSPITABLE WITH OUR NEW VISITORS.
WE MIGHT AS WELL HAVE PUT OUT AN INVITE AND A FEW CHAIRS.

WE CANNOT LET THEM DESTROY THESE HOMES UNCHALLENGED.
DO NOT WORRY MY FRIEND. WE SHALL NOT ABANDON THE VILLAGES TO THEIR FATE.
THAT IS ALL I ASK.
WE MUST BE STRATEGIC IN OUR EFFORTS. THIS SIZE OF OPPOSITION REQUIRES THOUGHT.
NO SIGN OF THE BIG BLUE FELLOW.
WE WOULD NOT BE SKULKING AROUND IF THERE WAS.
RIGHT ENOUGH... AND I THINK WE'VE BEEN SPOTTED... GET OUT OF HERE!
I WILL NOT RETREAT FROM MY HOMELAND AGAIN.
SORRY BOYS. NOT QUITE WHAT WE HAD IN MIND.
CALL IT A DRAW IF YOU RUN?
THEIR AGGRESSION IS QUELLED BY THE LIGHT OF THE ETHER... BUT I CANNOT HOLD THEM FOR LONG.
ENGUS, AIM LEFT. DO NOT LET THEM FLANK US.
I HAVE IT COVERED.

THE PEOPLE WILL LOSE EVERYTHING IF WE ABANDON NOW.
WE'LL LOSE OUR HEADS IF WE DON'T.
WE WILL NOT DESERT THE CLANS... BUT THE FORCE OF THE GUARDIANS MUST UNITE.
BLACK LEAF TO POISONED VINE, MAGIC OF THE DARK IS MINE.
WHAT SORCERY IS THIS?
DO NOT LET THE POISON TOUCH YOUR SKIN.
THE BEAR CLAW AXE HAS SEEN OFF NATURE'S FURY BEFORE.
LET US FIND OUR BROTHERS OF THE NORTH... WE LEAVE FOR THE SHADOWS.

FRONTIER WALL.
THE GAP THROUGH THE WALL...
...IT IS THE ONLY WAY.
BRING IT DOWN BEHIND YOU.
THEY SHALL NOT FOLLOW.
END THE PURSUIT. THEY SCURRY LIKE RATS... ENJOY THE SCENERY BEFORE IT IS SET TO RUIN.
THE EVER WATCHFUL SHADOW...

THE STONE OF DESTINY... THE BLUE STONES.
THE WOES OF THE MORTAL WORLD ARE NOT ENDED...
...TO THE MOUNTAIN OF ETHER WE TRAVEL.
THE IMMORTAL GUARDIAN CONTINUES HIS SLUMBER...
SNNNORRRE!
AT THE POINT OF OUR INCEPTION THE GUARDIANS CONVENE.
THE JOINING OF LIGHT AND SHADOW.
OUR BONDS STRENGTHEN AS WAR APPROACHES.

TRAGEDY FALLS ON THOSE WE PROTECT.
OUR LANDS SHARE THE SORROW OF LOSS.
A NOISE IN THE DARKNESS...
VAMPIRE OR SAXON, BE SWIFT IN YOUR EXECUTION.
SPEAK YOUR PURPOSE...
IT IS I, BRODE OF THE ISLES...
...I CLAIM THE SEAT OF MY ANCESTORS.
THE GUARDIANS OF SHADOW ARE WHOLE ONCE MORE...
...MAY YOU HAVE THE COURAGE OF YOUR FATHERS.
YOU WILL NEED IT BEFORE DARKNESS FALLS.

BATTLE BEGETS BELLIGERENCE BETWEEN BROTHERS.
THE VAMPIRE SCOURGE IS ENDED BUT LEAVES THE VALLEYS EMPTY OF LIFE...
...THOSE REMAINING HAVE FLED TO THE SAFETY OF THE RIVER CAVES.
A DIVERSION TO THE MENACE THAT BEFALLS US.
WE FACE THIS FOE ALONE...
DESERTED! THE VAUNTED GUARDIANS HIDE FROM TRUE POWER.
WE CONQUER THROUGH FEAR... WHEN THE SUN RISES, SURRENDER SHALL NOT HOLD OUR STEEL.
AT FIRST LIGHT WE DESCEND.
FOR A RUINOUS DAWN.
LET US MAKE READY.

ELTS ARE TIGHTENED...
BOOTS STRAPPED...
ARMOUR FIXED...
ARROWS STRAIGHTENED...
WEAPONS SHARPENED...
PRAYERS SPOKEN...

HEAR MY PRAYERS... WATCH OVER US WHERE GODS MAY NOT.
I CALL UPON ALL THAT IS GOOD AND TRUE IN THIS REALM, THAT OUR WORLDS MAY NOT SEE THEIR LIGHT EXTINGUISHED THIS DAY.

BENEATH THE *MOUNTAIN OF ETHER*.
CAMP OF THE MERCYAN ARMY.
BE VIGILANTE. THE WILDS ARE SAVAGE.
SHK.
SHK.
STAY FOCUSED.

THESE SAVAGES DARE TO CONFRONT THEIR NEW MASTER... DESTROY THEM!
YOU WILL NEED MORE THAN INSULTS.
THUD!
THUD!
THUD!
A MOMENT, MIGHTY KING.
AAAHHH!
...WHAT DO YOU WANT BOY? DO NOT VEX ME.
YOUR HELMET SIRE, IT IS RETRIEVED FROM THE NORTH.
NEVER APPROACH THE MERCYAN IN BATTLE... FURY COURSES THROUGH MY VEINS... GIVE IT TO ME!
GET OUT OF MY SIGHT!
CRACK!
OOOWWWHHH!!!
WIPE THEM OUT!
...LEAVE NOTHING BUT RUIN.
THE GUARDIANS SHALL FEAR THE MERCYAN.

ZZZZZZ...
DIIIEEE!!!
AN ENEMY OF SUCH HATE... THEY WILL NOT BE HELD FOR LONG.
LONG ENOUGH TO BURN.
HOLD THEM BACK...
...DO NOT GIVE GROUND.
NOT SEEN THIS MUCH ANGER SINCE THE FESTIVAL RAN OUT OF WHISKY.
I'M QUITE COMFY. DON'T FANCY SHIFTING.
HOLD OUR POSITION.

I CALL ON THE ONE THEY CALL THE HUNTER TO STAND AND FACE ME.
FINALLY, THIS COUNTRY BRINGS FORTH A CHALLENGER.
WE BRING MANY CHALLENGES TO YOUR DOOR, USURPER.
CHING!
DRIN
THE SERPENT BLADE ENDS THIS...
YOU ASSUME TOO MUCH, FOOL.
DRIINGG!!
NO... HOW?... UUUGH.
DO YOU FEEL THAT...? THAT IS YOUR COURAGE... SLIPPING AWAY.
YOU SHALL NOT LINGER LONG IN THESE LANDS.
LONGER THAN YOU, FIELD MOUSE.

THE HUNTER IS FALLEN.
GUARDIAN OF NOTHING!
AAAH! WHAT IS IT?
YOU SEE! THEIR BEST ARE NO MATCH FOR THE MERCYAN.

STAY STRONG. IT IS THE PASSING OF LOARN... WE FIGHT IN HIS HONOUR NOW.

GRUNT!
WIND WHISPERS WHILE WARRIORS WAIT IN WONDER.
THE SHADOW'S DEFIANT.
UNTIL OUR LIGHT FADES... THE *ETHEREAL REALM* STANDS WITH YOU.

AS WARRIORS FALL, FEAR FILLS MY MIND.
UNTIL THE *BLUE STONES* CALL, WE FIGHT.
MAY OUR FATHERS WATCH OVER US.
GIVE US THE COURAGE TO DIE WELL.
SMASH!
COVER THEM.
SCHOOM!
SCHOOM!
SCHOOM!
LET IT BE KNOWN THAT THE COURAGE OF CANO STOOD STRONG.

AMMUNITION RUNS LOW. BE SPARING.
THE YOUNG ONES ARE IN DANGER!
GET OUT OF THERE! RETREAT!
TAKE YOUR POSITIONS.
AIM!

BRODE! CANO! PROTECT YOUR BACK!
ENGUS! WATCH...!
...NO!!!
GET TO SAFETY...IT IS OVER FOR ME.
NOOOOOO!!!
HOLD ON! HELP IS... ENGUS!!!

I AM TOO LATE... THE RIVER MOURNS ITS CHAMPION.
COME GUARDIANS, KEEP YOUR DISCIPLINE.
I AM NOT DONE.
...TO THE END.
DEATH IS NOT THE END.
CALM YOURSELVES. A NATION DEPENDS ON US.
KEEP THEM SAFE. REGRET HANGS HEAVILY ON THEIR MINDS.
WE WILL WATCH OVER THEM.
FROM THE DEPTHS OF BATTLE I SUMMON THE LIGHT OF THE FAE.
THE ETHER HEEDS YOUR CALL.

THE ETHEREAL REALM...
...EILYS, ORACLE OF THE FAE.
I SUMMON THE ESSENCE OF ETHEREAL LIGHT.
THEY USE SORCERY AGAINST US....
...IMMORTAL MAGIC!
DESTRUCTION DETERMINES THE DAWN FROM A DIFFERENT DIMENSION.
THE SKY BRINGS SOLACE IN THE EYE OF THE STORM.

ZZZZZZ...
COUGH! ...SPLUTTER!
ACH! I FEEL DREADFUL... MY HEAD POUNDS.
HE LIGHT OF EILYS REJUVENATES.
I HAVE ABANDONED MY BROTHERS.
IN SEARCH OF REDEMPTION HE RETURNS...

TOO LONG HAVE I NEGLECTED MY DUTY.
BLEURGH!...
...I CANNOT SHAKE THIS INFERNAL STATE.
COME ON! GATHER YOURSELF!
HERE COMES TROUBLE!
THANK YOU EILYS.
SO... THEY THINK THEY HAVE A SAVIOUR.
THIS BATTLE IS FAR FROM OVER.
WE HAVE YET TO CALL THE DIVINE.
THE GODS *ARE* ON OUR SIDE.

HOLD THE LINE!
BATTLES IN STUPOR.
MY EYES DIZZY. I CANNOT STOP THIS SICKNESS.
YOU DO NOT STAND ALONE.
COME FORTH AND FIGHT!
YES!

WAR WAITS FOR NO MAN.
STAY CLOSE. FOLLOW OUR LEAD.
WE ARE WITH YOU...
...'TIL THE END.
UNITED THEY STAND...
...AGAINST THE BEAST OF TYRANNY
FORWARD!
SMASH!...
...CRACK!
MY ARMY BREAKS BEFORE ME.
YOU LOOK TO RULE THOSE WHO LIVE FREE.
I AM KING OF ALL MEN, IT IS MY RIGHT!
I AM NOT MAN...
AND NOT YOURS TO RULE.

YOUR RULE PROMISES DESTRUCTION, KING OF KINGS.
THE BLOOD OF MANNUS, THE FIRST ARYAN.
TO THE GOD OF ALL ARYANS WE VENERATE THIS LAND. IN WORSHIP OF TUISTO, CREATOR OF THE MASTER RACE.
SHE SUMMONS FROM THE EARTH.
MY MEN NEED THE POWER OF THE GODS.
OUR ASSAULT IS EFFECTIVE... BUT WE HAVE BROKEN NOTHING.

RISE... RISE NOW, ALL POWERFUL TUISTO.
A CACOPHONY FROM DEEP IN THE EARTH ...
I STILL SUFFER THIS AFFLICTION.
A DEITY OF DESTRUCTION DELIVERS THIS DOWNFALL.
WHAT IN THE WORLD BRINGS THIS NEW DEVILRY?
THIS IS NOT OF OUR WORLD.
AAAAAAAAAAAA......!!!

THE DEITY MANIFESTS IN STONE.
FEVER FILLS ME ONCE MORE.
AAAH!
GULP!
AAARRRGGG!!!
LOOK TO YOUR SAVIOUR...
...WATCH HIS FINAL BREATH.
"I CANNOT FAIL. BUT MY ENERGY IS SPENT."
MY HEAD! NO... I MUST...
ZZZ...

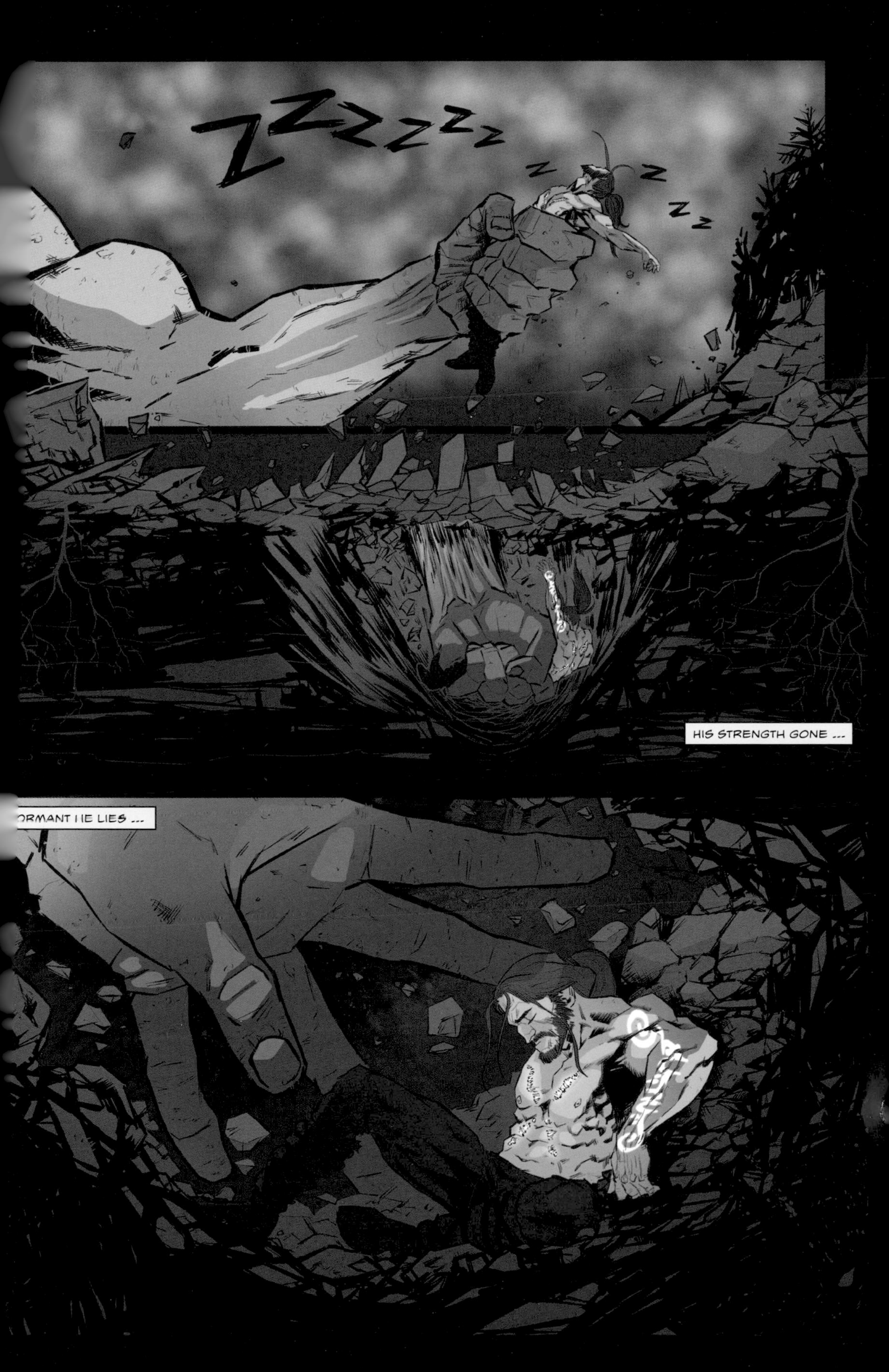
ZZZZZZZZ
Z Z Z Z
HIS STRENGTH GONE ...
ORMANT HE LIES ...

SALTIRE HAS HIS OWN BATTLE TO FIGHT NOW.
I'VE NOT SEEN A HAND THAT SCARY SINCE MY MOTHER CAUGHT ME STEALING.
THE LIGHT OF THE ETHER IS SPENT.
DO NOT LINGER... MOVE SWIFTLY.
AAAHHH...!
GO!
...WE ARE DONE.
THE PAIN OF LOSS GROWS.
WE ARE NOT THROUGH YET....
...GATHER YOUR SENSES, REMEMBER YOUR DUTY.

THE HIGHLAND CLANS ARE CONGREGATED IN A GLEN, UNPROTECTED. THE POPULATION SEEMS DECIMATED.
EXCELLENT. WE SHALL CLEANSE THIS FUTILE RACE FROM THE FACE OF THE EARTH.
THE TIME IS UPON US. WIPE THEM OUT!
WITH OUR CREATOR BEFORE US, YOU ARE THE TRUE SONS OF MANNAN....
...ATTACK!
WE MUST SEPARATE, LEAD THE SAXONS TO FOLLOW EACH OF US...
...HOPE THAT THIS SPIRIT WILL NOT HARM HIS OWN.
AGREED.
KRACK!
STAND AND FACE YOUR DESTINY, COWARDS. YOU CANNOT RUN FROM FATE...
...THE MERCYAN HUNTS YOU NOW.
THIS GUARDIAN STILL HOLDS THEIR GROUND.

"AS THE END NEARS..."
"...I SEEK PEACE AMID CHAOS."
HEAR MY PLEA...
...AS EVIL FALLS UPON US, ONCE MORE I ASK FOR THE LIGHT OF OUR WORLD.
THE PAIN THAT BEFALLS YOU, SO MUCH TO BEAR...
...OUR CHAMPION, LOST TO THE DARKNESS.
THE LIGHT YOU SEEK IS ALL BUT EXTINGUISHED, A FLICKER WITHIN THE SHADOWS.
FOR THE SAKE OF THIS WORLD...
...BEFORE ALL THAT IS RIGHT IS LOST.

THE SAXON MENACE IS RELENTLESS.
I CALL UPON ALL THAT IS LIGHT, COME FORTH IN THIS HOUR OF NEED.
I AM SQUANDERED...
LET US ANSWER YOUR PRAYERS FOR A QUICK DEATH.
WE DO NOT FEAR THE END.
IMPOSSIBLE... A DECEPTION!

THE DIE IS CAST AT THE END OF DAYS.
THE NORTHERN LIGHTS SHINE ONCE MORE.
THE ETHEREAL STAFF INFUSED.
MIGHT FATE ALLOW US ONE CHANCE.
HOLD! TURN YOUR ATTENTION TO THE SHADOWS.
A LITTLE LONGER...

THE LIGHT OF LL THAT IS PURE, AWAKEN OUR PROTECTOR!
STOP HIM! LISTEN TO ME, STOP THE IMMORTAL! HE PLOTS AGAINST US.
BRING ME THE HEAD OF THE FAE.
FREEDOM IS A MYTH PERPETUATED BY THE WEAK TO GIVE PURPOSE TO THEIR MEANINGLESS LIVES.
YOU UNDERSTAND NOTHING OF FREEDOM.
AND WHAT PLAN HAVE YOU FOR OUR PEOPLE?
PLAN? NO PLAN GUARDIAN. THEY WILL CEASE TO EXIST.

AND THE GUARDIANS SHALL BE FIRST TO BE FORGOTTEN.
WE DO NOT FIGHT FOR REMEMBRANCE.
IN THE DARKNESS OF THE EARTH...
WHERE ARE YOU YA BIG BLUE BAMPOT?
WE CAN ONLY HOPE HE IS NOT LOST.
UNYIELDING AGAINST THE POWER OF THE SHADOWS.
DO YOU THINK IT'S TOO LATE FOR AN APOLOGY?
THAT'S A FIRM HANDSHAKE.
RAPACIOUS ROOTS REACH TO RESTRICT THIS RUINOUS RAGE.

THE HOURGLASS RUNS EMPTY FOR YOU.
A SINGLE GRAIN OF SAND SEES HOPE REMAIN.
STEED OF MY FATHER.
NO BEAST CAN SAVE YOU NOW.
PACIFY THIS PETRIFIED POSSESSION...
...PURPOSEFULLY PURIFY THIS PERILOUS POLLUTION... OOMPH!
THE TIDE TURNS AGAINST US.
THE ETHER FAILS TO WAKEN OUR PROTECTOR...
...MAY COURAGE HOLD.

LET MY END NOT BE IN VAIN.
KEEP YOUR AIM FIXED.
WE HAVE HIM IN OUR SIGHTS SIRE.
HIS HEAD IS MINE...
...FACE YOUR FATE GUARDIAN!
HOLD THE BEAST BACK!
SNARL!
THE CRY OF BATTLE STILL CALLS.
MY BROTHER WILL NOT FALL WITHOUT QUARREL.

E CREATURES OF THE
RTH... ILLUMINATED.
CRAWL!
CREEP!
SQUIRM!
WHAT FURTHER SHADES THIS DESOLATE PLACE.
ROOOAAARRR!!!...

AAAAAAHHH!!!
FIRE FROM THE SKY... A HARMFUL OMEN.
CRACK!
I SPEND THE LAST OF MY ARROWS.
THE FATE OF THIS LAND IS COME AT LAST...
...AND FORTUNE FAVOURS THE MERCYAN.
DO NOT PERISH HERE.
ROOOAAARRR!!
THE SPIRIT OF MY BROTHERS BRINGS HOPE.
AS WE ENDURE, OUR ADVERSARY GROWS WEARY...
...AND ENDURE WE SHALL.

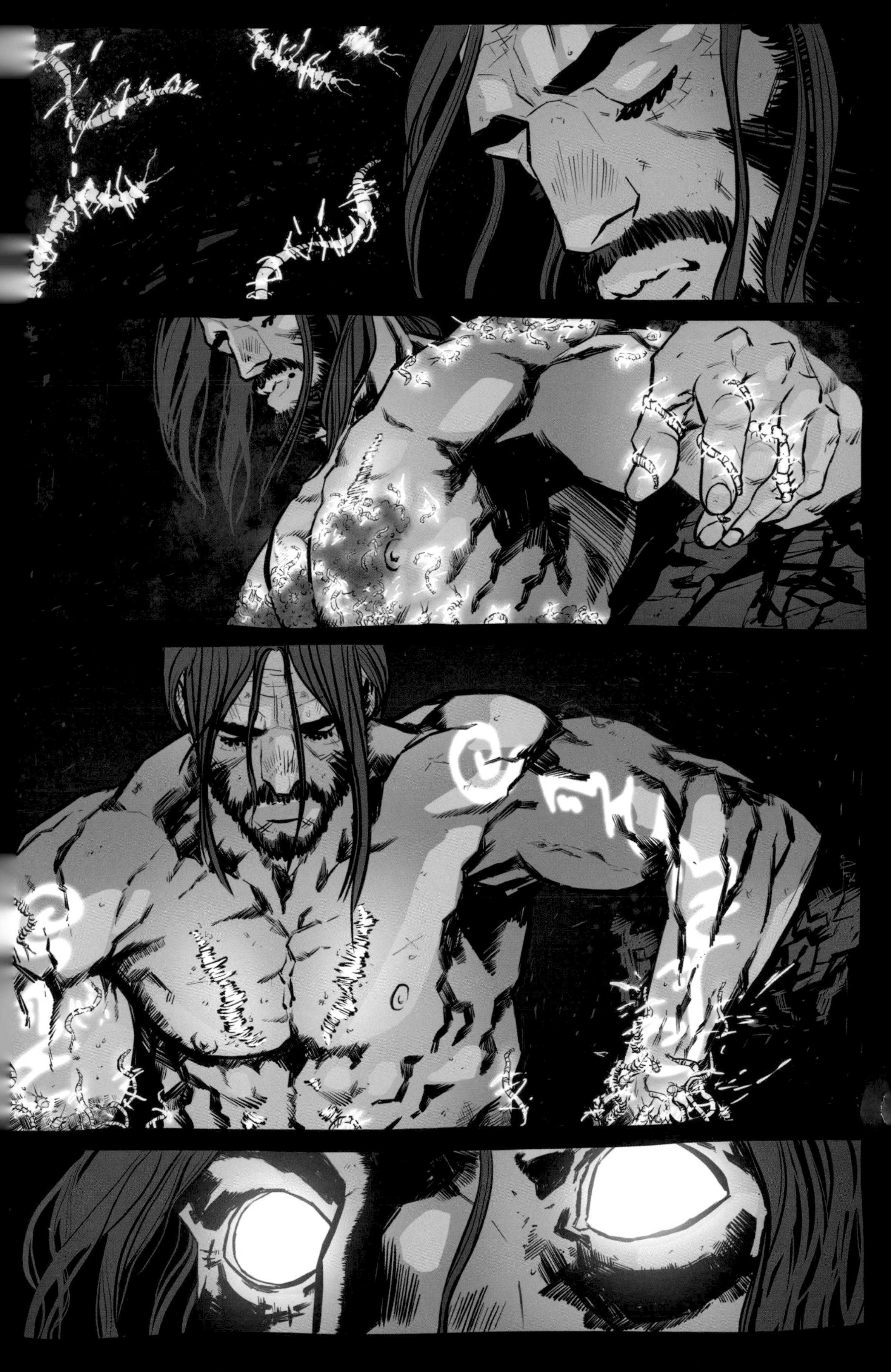

STAND! STAND NOW AND BE COUNTED.
ENGEANCE UNLEASHED!
YOUR REIGN OF TERROR IS OVER!

THOSE WHO WAGE WAR...
FEEL MY WRATH!
AAAAAAAAA...
MAGNETIC DIAMONDSTEEL!

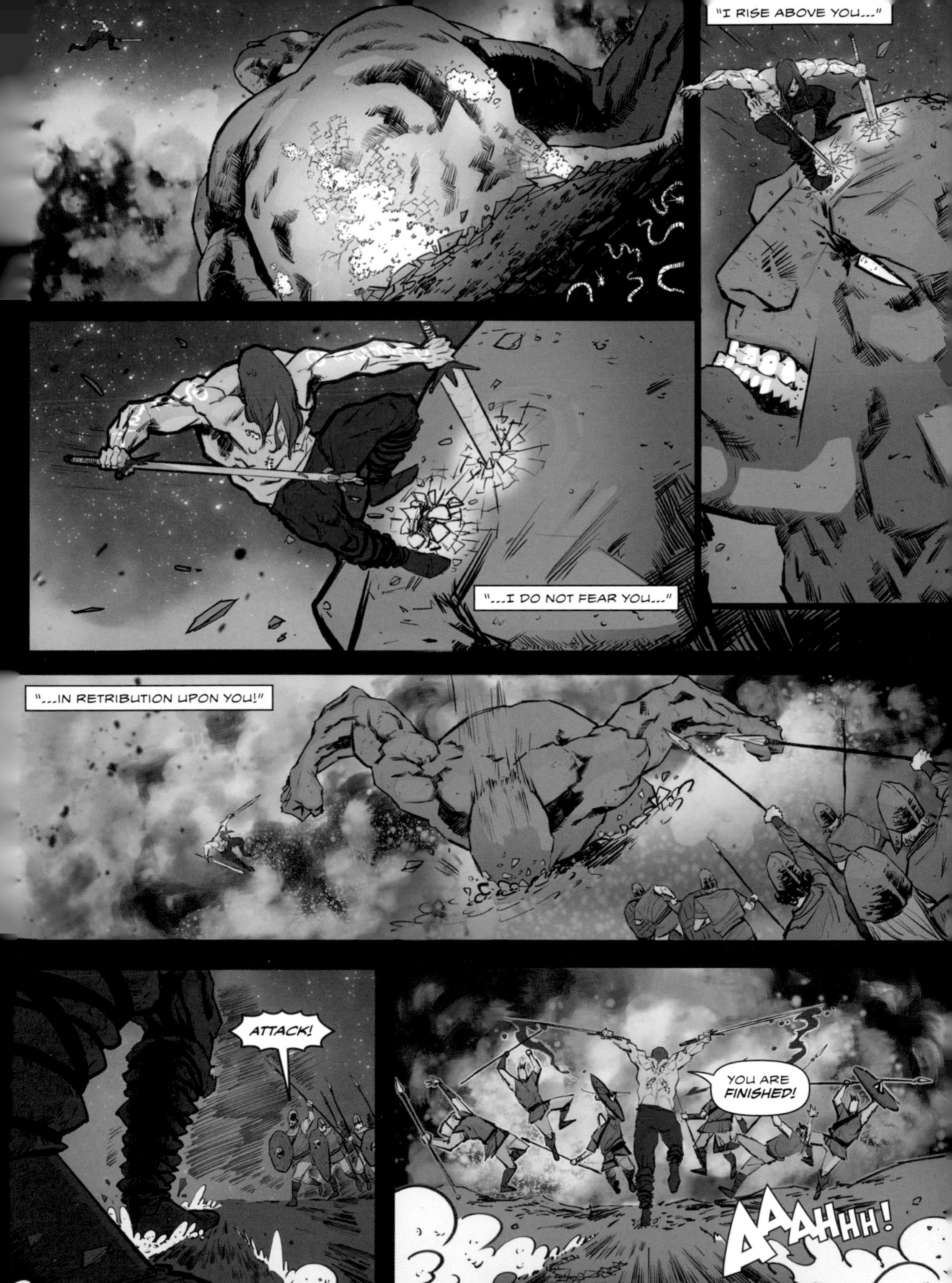
"I RISE ABOVE YOU..."
"...I DO NOT FEAR YOU..."
"...IN RETRIBUTION UPON YOU!"

ATTACK!
YOU ARE FINISHED!
AAAHHH!

BE SWIFT. THE SHADOWS HUNT OUR CAPTOR NOW.
LEAVE THIS MORTAL TO ME.
MORTAL!? HA! I WILL BE REMEMBERED THROUGH THE AGES.
THE CELESTIAL BODIES ALIGN NO LONGER.
ALL SHALL BOW BEFORE THE MERCYAN.
YOUR FURY BURNS...
...BUT I AM BORN OF FIRE.

AAH! RELEASE ME, HEATHEN.
THE BAIT IS TAKEN.
I AM THE INVINCIBLE... THE RULER OF KINGS...
... I CAN... I CAN OFFER YOU... POWER OVER THIS DOMINION!
YOUR INFLUENCE WANES AMONG THE SHADOWS.
I HOLD MORE POWER THAN ALL YOUR KINGS.
GULF! CONSIDER MY OFFER MORE THOROUGHLY... P... P... PLEASE.
FATE CALLS YOU FORTH TO ANSWER FOR THIS WAR.
SPARE US AND I WILL HALT THIS. ONLY I CAN REVERSE IT.

STEADY...
TO RECLAIM THE ETHEREAL STAFF.
WE MUST BE BOLD.
IT COMES TO THIS...
I AM A PRISONER OF THIS VILE TYRANT...
...OH, THAT YOU WOULD SPARE MY INSIGNIFICANT LIFE.
WRETCHED HAG! YOU WILL RUE THIS BETRAYAL.

DO NOT MEDDLE WITH ME, *WITCH.*

BASH!
I WILL BRING YOU DOWN!
AAAHHH!!!
I HAVE IT IN MY SIGHTS. *STAND CLEAR!*
"MAY THE LIGHT GUIDE YOU."

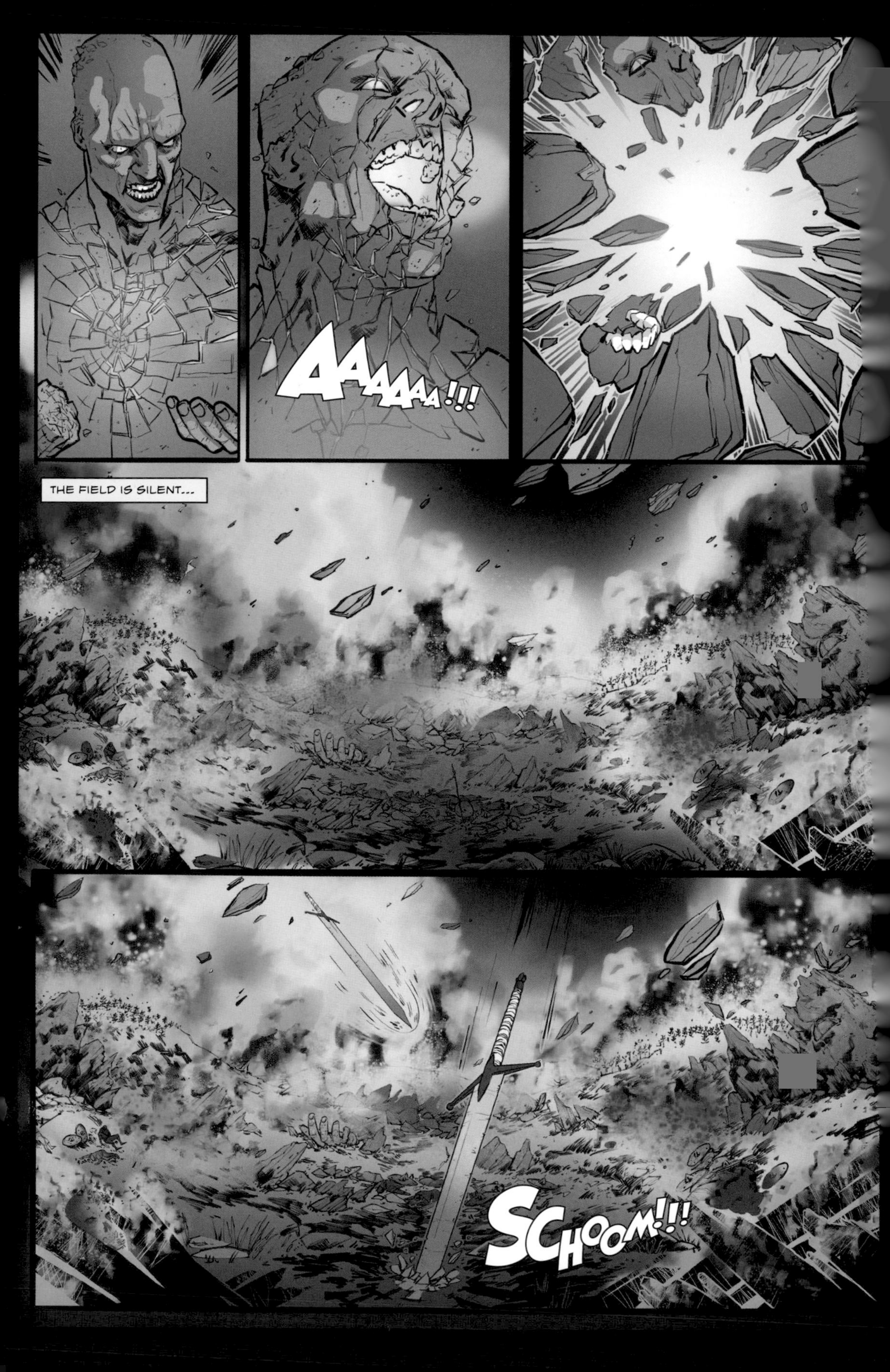
AAAAAA!!!
THE FIELD IS SILENT...
SCHOOM!!!

THE FIERCEST ENEMY THIS LAND HAS KNOWN LIES AT OUR FEET.
I'VE SEEN FOLK FALL APART AT BIG BLUE, BUT THIS ONE TAKES SOME BEATING.

YOU CANNOT ESCAPE THE SHADOWS.
LET ME GO!
HA! FEEL DEATH COARSE YOUR VEINS!
NO! YOU ARE ENDED! HOW CAN THIS BE?
YOUR SORCERY IS FOR THE LIVING.
A DECISION...
...ON SHE WHO CREATED THIS CARNAGE.
WE MUST CARE FOR THE SHAMAN, HE NEEDS REST.
A TRIUMPH OF SPIRIT.

WE MAY JUDGE HER, BUT WE ARE NOT EXECUTIONERS. THIS LAND LIVES ON PRINCIPLES GREATER THAN THOSE THAT WOULD SEEK TO RULE US.
BE WARY OF THIS ONE, A TORMENTED SOUL.
I WON'T BE ASKING HER OUT FOR THE EVENING IF THAT'S YOUR WORRY.
WHY DOES HE LINGER?
HE SEEKS THE FALLEN.
THE BODIES OF THE GUARDIANS DESERVE THEIR LAST RIGHTS.

ONCE MORE WE REMEMBER THOSE WHO GAVE THEIR LIVES.
THE COST OF FREEDOM...

E GUARDIANS SEEK
T THEIR CLANS...
...THEIR HOMES.
RDENED BY THE
ROCITIES OF WAR.
SAFE HOME, SEA BEARER. NO DRINKING AND SAILING.
THEY LONG FOR THE MOUNTAIN SOLITUDE.
LET US HOPE OUR RESILIENCE RESONATES IN THE NEW EMPIRES OF THE WORLD.
CONSIDER THIS CONFLICT THE CAUSE OF THE CALM CREATED.
THE SHADOW BEARER RETURNS TO THE DARKNESS.
UNTIL WE ARE CALLED FORTH ONCE MORE I PRAY FOR ENDURING PEACE.
TO THE REALM OF LIGHT THEY TRAVEL.
MAY THEY NE'ER SEE THE SUN RISE ON DAYS SUCH AS THESE.
A NEW BREED IS BROUGHT TO PASS.

INO - ENTRANCE TO THE ETHEREAL WORLD.
THE ETHEREAL REALM WELCOMES YOU.
THE LIGHT OF THE ORACLE... EXTINGUISHED.
GO TO HER. SEEING YOU WILL BRING COMFORT.
SHE IS SO WEAK. I CANNOT HIDE MY SORROW AT HER FRAILTY.
BE STRONG... FOR HER SAKE...
...LET HER SEE YOU.

A SADNESS FILLS YOU...
...LET NOT THE FAILINGS OF MY FLESH BRING DESPAIR.
WORRY NOT FOR WHAT THE FUTURE HOLDS. THE LIGHT OF THE ETHER TAKES ALL TO THAT WHICH WILL EVER BE.
YOUR TOUCH SOOTHES EVEN THE DEEPEST SCARS.
THIS IS MY DOING. YOU DID THIS TO SAVE ME.
I DID THIS TO SAVE OUR LAND, OUR PEOPLE. YOU ARE THEIR SAVIOUR.
I HAVE SOMETHING FOR YOU.
A GIFT FROM THE MORTAL WORLD?
HOW CAN THIS BE?
I RETURN THE LIGHT TO YOU.
I AM BLESSED TO SEE YOU WELL ONCE MORE.

THE HIGHLANDS OF SHADOW.
THE VALLEYS OF LIGHT.
WE RETURN TO PEACE AS THE FURY OF WAR SUBSIDES...
...EVER WATCHFUL...

LAND OF THE FREE.

THE NORTH SEA...
...COAST OF THE NORSE LANDS.